MAKE A WISH

WORLD OF READING

MAKE A WISH

P. DAVID PEARSON   DALE D. JOHNSON

THEODORE CLYMER   ROSELMINA INDRISANO   RICHARD L. VENEZKY

JAMES F. BAUMANN   ELFRIEDA HIEBERT   MARIAN TOTH

Consulting Authors

CARL GRANT   JEANNE PARATORE

SILVER BURDETT & GINN

NEEDHAM, MA • MORRISTOWN, NJ
ATLANTA, GA • CINCINNATI, OH • DALLAS, TX
MENLO PARK, CA • NORTHFIELD, IL

ALL ABOUT ANIMALS

READERS' CHOICE

Let's Pretend

 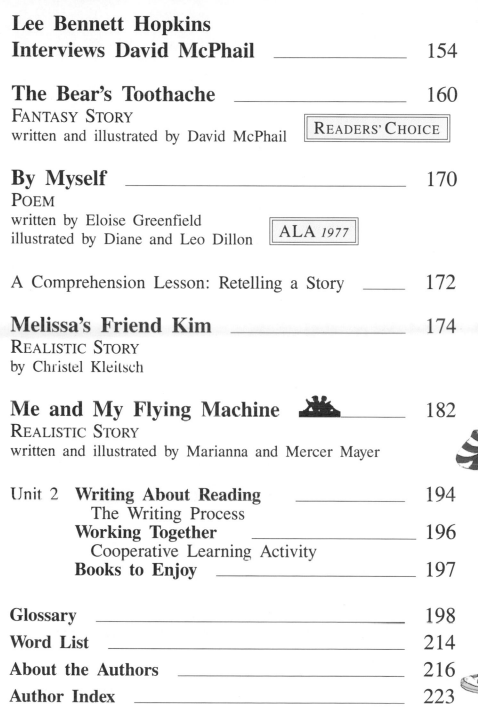

ALL ABOUT ANIMALS

Some animals are real, and some are make-believe.

Why do we like stories about animals?

CAROUSEL HORSE,
wood carving by Illions,
American, c. 1923

A Morning in Fall
by Reeve Lindbergh

Many kinds of animals live on a farm. Early in the morning, some animals are already busy.

This is the farm on a morning in fall.
The sun has come over the hill.
Come and see who is sleeping and who is not,
When the farm in the morning looks still.

Puppies will sleep this morning in fall.
Puppies sleep late on the farm.
One sleeping brother stays close to his mother.
It makes him feel happy and warm.

The cat is not sleeping this morning in fall.
The cat sees the cows going out.
She waits for the sun on a morning that's fun.
She likes to be up and about.

Cows are not sleeping this morning in fall.
In the morning the cows go outside.

Take a calf for a run
  and have all kinds of fun.
Take him back to his
  warm mother's side.

Sheep are not sleeping this
   morning in fall.
You can run with the
   sheep down the hill.
You may find one sheep who
   is so good and so kind,
When you give her a hug
   she stays still.

Pigs are not sleeping this morning in fall.
Morning sun is good for a pig.
Pigs like to play and to sleep in the day.
The warm sun will help them get big.

This is the farm on a morning in fall,
When the sun has come over the hill.
You have seen who is sleeping and
   who is not,
When the farm in the morning looks still.

What Do You Think?

Would you like to be on a farm in the morning? Tell why or why not.

A Morning in Fall

 ## Questions

1. How did the farm look in the morning?
2. Which animals were awake in the morning? Which animals were still sleeping?
3. What season of the year is it? How do you know?

 ## Writing to Learn

THINK AND DECIDE   Whose eyes are closed this morning in fall? Draw a picture. Show someone or something who might be sleeping.

WRITE   Write what you see in your picture.

THINKING

READING
THINKING
WRITING

CONNECTION

A Strategy for Thinking:

Asking "Who?"

How can you remember a story? One way is to ask, "Who is in the story?"

You have read "A Morning in Fall."

Look at the pictures. Who was in the story?

Does your answer help you remember the story?

20

Read the poem below. Ask yourself, "Who is in the poem?"

> Jack be nimble,
> Jack be quick,
> Jack jumped over
> The candlestick.

Who is in the poem?

Next you will read "Who Took the Farmer's Hat?"

Ask yourself, "Who is in the story?"

◆◆◆ The writing connection can be found on page 53.

Who Took the Farmer's Hat?

by Joan Nodset

These animals see many things,
but not the farmer's hat.

The farmer had a hat.
He had an old brown hat.
Oh, how he liked that old brown hat!

But the wind took the farmer's hat,
and away it went.

The farmer ran to look for it.
He looked and he looked and he looked.
Where was the farmer's hat?

The farmer saw Squirrel.
"Squirrel, did you see
my old brown hat?" said the farmer.

"No," said Squirrel.
"I saw a round brown bird.
I saw a bird with no wings."

Who is this?

Who is this?

23

The farmer saw Mouse.
"Mouse, did you see
my old brown hat?" said the farmer.

Who is this?

"No," said Mouse.
"I saw a big brown hole.
It looked like a mouse hole.
I ran to the hole, but away it went."

24

The farmer saw Goat.
"Goat, did you see
my old brown hat?" said the farmer.

"No," said Goat.
"I saw a round brown pot.
I wanted to eat it.
But Bird took that pot away."

The farmer saw Bird.
"Bird, did you take
my old brown hat?" said the farmer.

"No," said Bird.
"I saw this round brown nest,
but no hat."

The farmer looked
at the nest in the tree.
It was an old round brown nest.

Bird was in it.
Bird had the farmer's hat!

"Oh, my!" said the farmer.

"Do you like my nest?" said Bird.

"I likc it," said the farmer.
"Oh, I like that round brown nest.
It looks a little like my old brown hat.
But I see it is a round brown nest."

Who took
the
farmer's
hat?

The farmer has a new brown hat.

Oh, how he likes that new brown hat!

Bird has an old brown nest.

Oh, how Bird likes that old brown nest! ◆◆◆

 What Do You Think?

What was the funniest part of this story? Tell why you think so.

Who Took the Farmer's Hat?

Questions

1. How did the farmer lose his hat?
2. What did the goat think the farmer's hat was?
3. Is this story real or make-believe? How do you know?
4. Why do you think the bird used the hat for a nest?

Writing to Learn

THINK AND IMAGINE If you saw the farmer's hat, what would it look like to you? On a sheet of paper, draw what you think it would look like.

WRITE Look at your picture. Label the things you see.

ABC Books

▲ armadillo

Animals can help you learn your ABCs. Look at these pages from ABC books. This ABC book shows you a letter. It shows a picture of an animal. The name of the animal begins with that letter.

The bear is playing a banjo under the letter B.

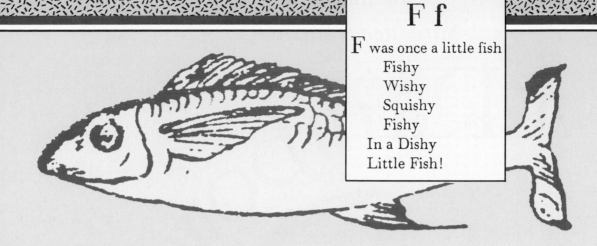

F f

F was once a little fish
Fishy
Wishy
Squishy
Fishy
In a Dishy
Little Fish!

Fish starts with the letter F. Some ABC books show more than one word that starts with the same letter.

Swan starts with the letter S. You can learn your ABCs from these friendly animals.

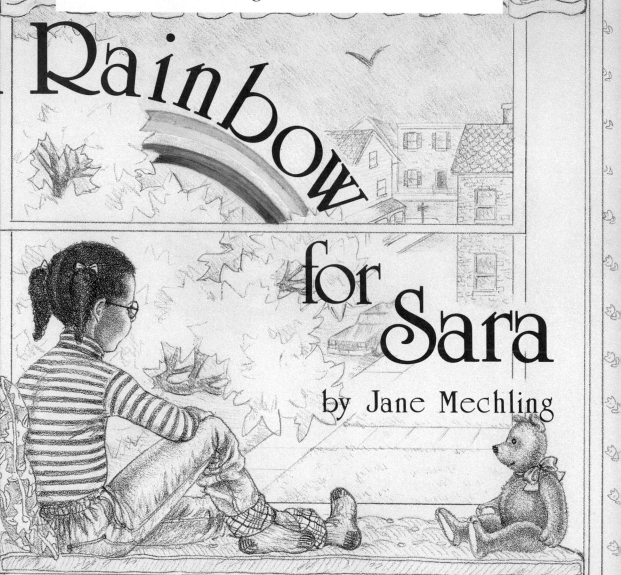

In this story, no one knows why Sara needs string.

A Rainbow for Sara

by Jane Mechling

Sara sat and sat, looking out at the big tree. She looked at her mother and asked, "Mom, do you have some string?"

"Yes, here is some red string,"
said Sara's mother. "Is it for
your hair?"

"No," said Sara. "It's not
for my hair."

"I know," said Mother. "You
are going to fix something with it."

"No," said Sara. "You'll see."

Sara saw that her father had some string, too. She asked him for it.

"Here you are," said her father. "Do you need it to put around a box?"

"No," said Sara. "You'll see."

"I know," said Father. "You are going to fly your kite with it."

"No," Sara said. "I am thinking of something else."

Sara ran outside to play with Peter
and Anna.

"I am keeping string in a box,"
said Sara.

"I have some string in my pocket.
You may have it," said Peter.

"You are keeping string?"
said Anna. "What are you going
to do with all that string? Will
you and your cat play with it?"

"No," said Sara. "You'll see."

Soon Sara had all the string she needed. She had red string, orange string, green string, and yellow string. She had purple string, too! Sara put all her string near the big tree and waited.

She waited and waited. Then she waited some more. She waited until it was time for bed.

In the morning, Sara's mom asked,
"Where is all your string?"

"Come with me," said Sara.
She got her dad, and Peter and
Anna, too.

"Look!" said Sara.

"Oh my!" said Sara's dad.
"Your string helped a bird make
her nest."

Sara's mother said, "And look!
The bird made a rainbow for Sara!"

What Do You Think?

How do you think Sara felt about
the bird's nest?

A Rainbow for Sara

Questions

1. What was Sara collecting?
2. Why did Sara ask everybody for string?
3. Do you think Sara was helping the bird? What makes you think so?
4. What was Sara's rainbow?

Writing to Learn

THINK AND DECIDE   Sara uses string in many ways. How do you use string?

> Ways to use string
>
> 1. to wrap a gift
> 2. as hair ribbon
> 3.

WRITE   Take out a sheet of paper. Make a list like Sara's list above. Your list will tell how you use string.

How to Help Make a Bird's Nest

by Marion de Barenne

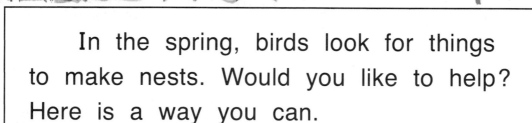

In the spring, birds look for things to make nests. Would you like to help? Here is a way you can.

Tie two or three pine cones together like this.

Cut some string.
Put it on the pine cones like this.

Then tie the pine cones to a tree.
The birds will take the string
to make a nest!

What Does Little Birdie Say?

What does little birdie say,
In her nest at peep of day?
   "Let me fly," says little birdie,
"Mother, let me fly away."

Birdie, rest a little longer,
Till the little wings are stronger.
So she rests a little longer,
   Then she flies away.

44

What does little baby say,
In her bed at peep of day?
    Baby says, like little birdie,
"Let me rise and fly away."

Baby, sleep a little longer,
Till the little limbs are stronger.
If she sleeps a little longer,
    Baby, too, shall fly away.

Alfred, Lord Tennyson

Polar Bear Leaps

written by Derek Hall
illustrated by John Butler

*Animals can live anywhere. Meet
an animal that lives where it is always
cold.*

It is time for Polar Bear to come
out of the den where he was born.
For the first time he plays outside
in the snow.

As his mother eats, Polar Bear
runs off. The small bear stands up
on his back legs to look out over
the ice. Then, the ice breaks!

A small bit of ice takes Polar Bear away from his mother. He sees his mother and calls out to her for help.

Mother Bear calls back as she runs
to him. The small bear leaps over the
hole in the ice. His back legs slip
into the water.

Just in time Polar Bear's mother
grabs him by the neck. The water drips
off him as she pulls him from the water.
Polar Bear is safe now.

Now it is time for Polar Bear
to eat. Mother Bear feeds him.
Then he snuggles up close to her
and sleeps.

What Do You Think?

Do you think Polar Bear should
have run off by himself? Tell why or
why not.

Polar Bear Leaps

 ## Questions

1. Why did the ice begin to break?
2. What does Polar Bear need to learn before he grows up?
3. How did the story end?
4. Polar Bear lives in a place where it is always cold. How do you know this?

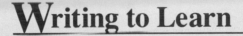 ## Writing to Learn

THINK AND TELL Think about "Polar Bear Leaps." *Who* was in the story? What did they do? Look at the words below.

Who?	Did What?
Little Polar Bear	leaped.
Polar Bear's Mother	saved him.

WRITE Write one or two sentences. Tell *who* did what in this story.

Literature:
Plays

Did you know that stories can be told in many ways? One way to tell a story is to act it out. When you act out a story, it is called a play.

Here is a picture of some children in a play. They act out a story as we listen and watch.

Did you know that puppet shows, movies, and most TV shows are kinds of plays?

The next story is written as a play. You will
see pictures of children acting out the story. As you
read the play, think about which animal you would
like to be.

Can you think of another way to act out the
story? Could it be a movie or a TV show?

The
Three Little Pigs

adapted by Adam Burdick

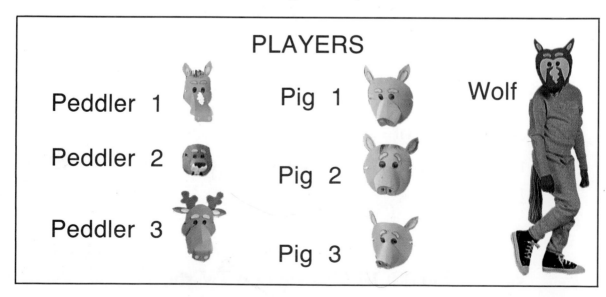

PLAYERS

Peddler 1

Peddler 2

Peddler 3

Pig 1

Pig 2

Pig 3

Wolf

There are different ways to keep a wolf away.

Peddler 1: Straw! Straw for sale!
One corncob for a bale!

Peddler 2: Get your sticks! Just cut!
Sticks for sale!

Peddler 3: Bricks! Just six corncobs!

Pig 1: I think I will make my house
from straw. Straw is strong.
Please give me some straw.

Pig 2: I think I will make my house
from sticks. Sticks are
stronger than straw. Please
give me some sticks.

Pig 3: I will make my house from
bricks. Bricks cost more,
but they are the strongest
of all. Please give me
some bricks.

Pig 1: What a fine house
I have made.

Wolf: Knock, knock.

Pig 1: Who is it?

Wolf: It's a friend. Little pig,
little pig, please, let me in.

Pig 1: Not by the hair on my
chinny chin chin.

Wolf: Then I'll huff, and I'll puff,
and I'll blow your house in!

Pig 1: Help! Help! The wolf is
here. I will run to my
sister's house. Her stick house
will keep me safe.

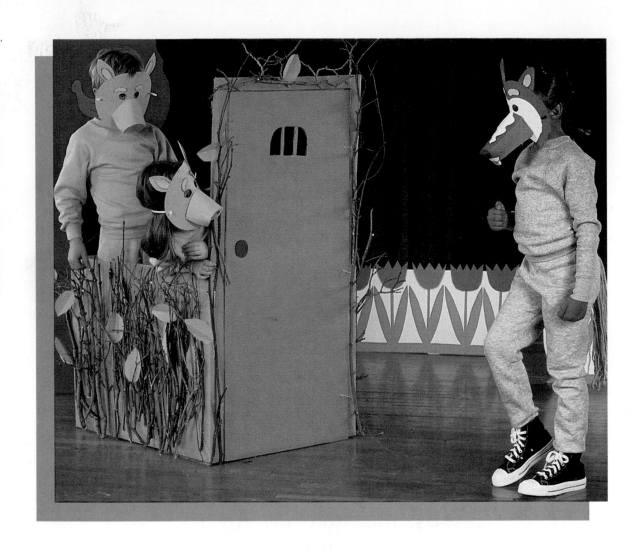

Pig 1: Sister, please, let me in!
The wolf blew my house
down!

Pig 2: Please, come in. My house
of sticks will keep you safe.

Wolf: Knock, knock.

Pig 2: Who is it?

Wolf: It's a friend. Little pig, little pig, please, let me in.

Pigs 1 & 2: Not by the hairs on our chinny chin chins.

Wolf: Then I'll huff, and I'll puff, and I'll blow your house in!

Pig 2: We can run to our big sister's house. Her brick house will keep us safe.

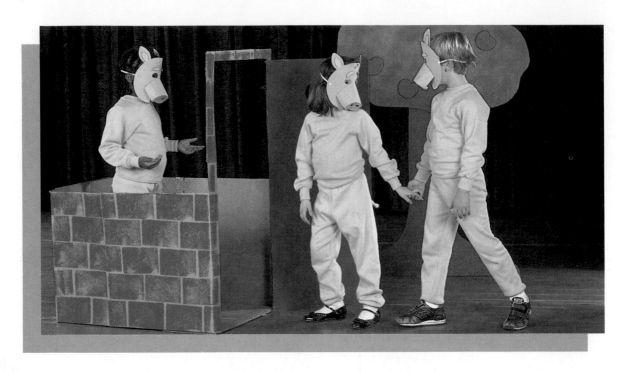

Pigs 1 & 2: Knock, knock.

Pig 3: Can I help you?

Pig 1: The wolf blew down
my straw house.

Pig 2: The wolf blew down
my stick house.

Pigs 1 & 2: Can we come in with you?

Pig 3: Please, do come in. You will
be safe in my strong brick
house.

Wolf: Knock, knock.

Pig 3: Who is it?

Wolf: It's a friend. Little pig,
little pig, please, let me in.

Pigs 1, 2, Not by the hairs on our
and 3: chinny chin chins.

Wolf: Then I'll huff, and I'll puff,
and I'll blow your house in.

63

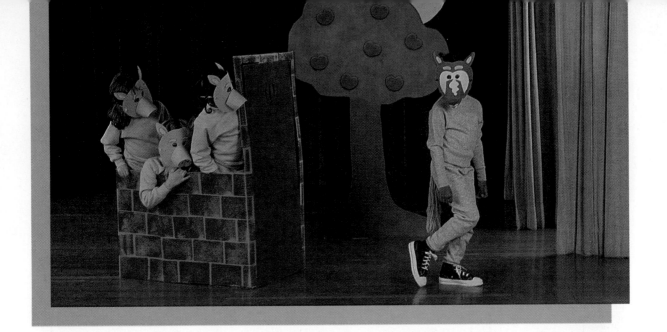

Pig 3: My house is too strong.
You cannot blow it in.

Wolf: Huff, puff! Huff, puff!
Huff, puff! Huff, puff!
Just one more time will
blow this house down!
HUFFFFFFF, PUFFFFFF.
Oh, I give up! This house
is too strong!

What Do You Think?

Would you like to live in a
house made from straw or sticks?
Tell why.

The
Three Little Pigs

 ## Questions

1. What do you think Pig 1 and Pig 2 will use to build their houses next time? Tell why you think this.
2. How are straw and sticks alike?
3. Which Pig's house did the wolf knock at first, second, and last?

 ## Writing to Learn

THINK AND PRETEND Pretend that you are going to make a new house. What would you use to build it? Draw a picture of your new house.

WRITE Write what would happen if the wolf came to your house.

Under a Stone
by Aileen Fisher

In the middle of a meadow
we turned up a stone
and saw a little village
we never had known,
with little streets and tunnels
and ant-folk on the run,
all frightened and excited
by the sudden burst of sun.

We watched them rushing headlong,
and then put back the stone
to cover up the village
we never had known,
to roof away the tunnels
where ants were on the run
before they got all sunburned
in the bright hot sun.

People build and live in many different kinds of homes. Animals do, too.

A World of Animals

by Susan Schroeder

The world is home for many animals.
All animals need a place to live.

You can find animals under the
ground, in the sky, and in the water.
Animals live all around us.

69

Turtles live on land and in water.
All turtles have a shell. The shell is
a home for the turtle. Some turtles can
hide in their shells.

Ducks make their homes near water. Ducks swim in the water and look for food. They make nests out of grass and mud near the water. The grass around the water hides their nests.

Some rabbits make their homes in meadows. They dig holes under the ground. Then they make nests out of their fur. Under the ground, the rabbits are warm and safe.

Many birds make their homes in trees. They fly to the ground to find things for their nests. They take the grass, sticks, and mud to the trees to make their nests. Birds are safe in their homes in the trees.

All animals need a place to
live. There are many animal homes
in the world. Look around you.
What animals live near you?

 ## What Do You Think?

Do you think a turtle would want
to live in a duck's nest? Tell why or
why not.

A World of Animals

Questions

1. Name three places where animals make their homes.
2. How are the homes of a duck and a rabbit alike? How are they different?
3. Name two things that help you know that this is a real story. What makes you think so?

Writing to Learn

THINK AND REMEMBER Think of the most interesting animal that you have ever seen. Draw a picture of your animal in a home.

WRITE Label the parts of your picture.

75

The *Months*

by Sara Coleridge

January brings the snow;
Makes our feet and fingers glow.

   February brings the rain;
   Thaws the frozen pond again.

March brings wind so cold and chill;
Drives the cattle from the hill.

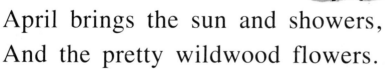

   April brings the sun and showers,
   And the pretty wildwood flowers.

May brings grass and leafy trees,
Waving in each gentle breeze.

June brings roses, fresh and fair,
And the cherries, ripe and rare.

July brings the greatest heat,
Cloudless skies and dusty street.

August brings the golden grain;
Harvest time begins again.

Mild September brings us more
Fruit and grain, for winter store.

Brown October brings the last
Of ripening gifts, from summer past.

Dull November brings the blast;
Down from the trees the leaves fall fast.

Cold December ends the rhyme
With blazing fires and holiday times.

Rabbits are usually faster than turtles, but not always.

The Hare
and the Tortoise

adapted by Ramón Martinez

Tortoise went out for a walk in the city. When he came to the park, he saw his friend, Hare.

"It is nice to see you, friend," said Hare. "Where are you going?"

"I am out for a walk," said Tortoise.

"That's nice," said Hare.

"Will you walk with me, Hare?" said Tortoise.

"Oh, no!" said Hare. "Rabbits don't walk. Rabbits run as fast as the wind!"

"As fast as the wind?" asked Tortoise.

"As fast as the wind," said Hare.
"Don't you believe me? Then I'll
show you. Will you race with me
around the city and back to the park?"

"I don't mind if I do,"
said Tortoise. "You may be as fast as
the wind, but you aren't the best."

So Hare and Tortoise had a race.
Off ran Hare as fast as the wind.

Now Hare was fast, but not very wise. He did not believe that Tortoise could win the race. So when he came to a bench at a bus stop, he sat down.

"I have lots of time," he said, "and I am tired. I will take a little nap."

So Hare went to sleep.

Now Tortoise was not very fast, but he did not stop. On and on he went. Tortoise was very tired, but he did not stop.

Tortoise came to the bus stop. There he saw his friend, Hare.

"Oh, my," Tortoise said. "Hare is sleeping. I'll keep going. I know I can win this race."

When Hare woke up he looked
for Tortoise. Tortoise was not in
back of him. Hare did not see
Tortoise at all.

"Where is Tortoise?" said Hare.
"I will go to the park. I will win
the race."

Hare ran to the park. Tortoise
was waiting for him.

"You have won the race!" said Hare to Tortoise. "I can run as fast as the wind! How did you win the race?"

"You may run faster, but I do not stop when I run," said Tortoise. "You cannot win a race if you stop."

"I think I will stop now. May I sit with you on this bench?" said Hare.

"I don't mind if you do," said Tortoise.

 ## What Do You Think?

Did you want the Hare or the Tortoise to win the race? Tell why.

The **Hare** and the **Tortoise**

 ## Questions

1. Who was faster at the beginning of the race? Who was faster at the end?
2. How did Tortoise win the race?
3. What might have happened if Hare had not taken a nap? Why do you think this?

 ## Writing to Learn

THINK AND DECIDE   Hare and Tortoise had a race. Draw a picture to show your favorite part of this race.

WRITE   Write a sentence to tell why Tortoise won the race.

Mercy, Percy!

by Else Holmelund Minarik

"Parsnips," said Percy, drumming
on the table. "I want parsnips. I want
to eat parsnips."

"Mother," said Percy. "Will you cook parsnips for me?"

"Mercy, Percy!" said mother. "We have no parsnips. Will bark bits do?"

No, Percy did not want bark bits.
Percy wanted parsnips.

"I want parsnips," said Percy.
He drummed on the table.

"Stop drumming the table!" said
Mother. "Here is your grandpa."

"Grandpa, Percy wants to eat
parsnips. I have no parsnips. Do you
have any parsnips?" said Mother.

"Oh, yes!" said Grandpa. "I have fine parsnips in my garden. My parsnips are the best! Come with me, Percy. We will get the parsnips. Then we can help mother cook them for you."

They came to the garden. Percy looked about. He saw some strawberries. He ate them.

And he saw some gooseberries, some big fine gooseberries. He began to eat the gooseberries.

Now gooseberry bushes are sticky.
But that did not stop Percy.

"I like it here," said Percy.
"I like to be stuck in sticky bushes,
with big fine gooseberries to eat."

Percy ate a lot of gooseberries.

Grandpa pulled up his parsnips. And then he pulled Percy out of the bushes.

"Percy," said Grandpa, "you will have a gooseberry tummy ache."

Grandpa was right. Percy did have a gooseberry tummy ache.

Percy cried, "All I wanted was parsnips!"

Mother said, "Parsnips will have to wait." She patted Percy's tummy.

Percy waited.

Then he was fine. His tummy ache went away.

"I am fine now, Mother," he said. "I am ready for parsnips."

"Good for you," said Mother.

She cooked the parsnips and Percy ate them.

"Mercy, Percy!" said mother. "Do you want more?"

"Yes," said Percy.

"I'll have some too," said Grandpa.

Mother said, "Well then, so will I."

So they had a family parsnip party!

Percy did not get a parsnip tummy ache. Not Percy! But then, no one ever gets a parsnip tummy ache.

What Do You Think?

Why do you think Percy didn't listen to Grandpa?

Writing an Ad

You have just read some stories about animals. Pretend one of those animals is yours. One day your pet gets lost. How could you let people know that you have lost your pet? One way is to write a ''lost and found'' ad.

Getting Ready

A ''lost and found'' ad tells what you have lost and how people can return it. Use the box below to plan your ad.

Question	Your answer
1. What kind of pet have you lost?	
2. What is your pet's name?	
3. What does it look like?	
4. What should people do if they find it?	

Writing

Now write your "lost and found" ad. You may want to draw a picture of your pet.

Listening to My Writing

Read your ad to a partner. Does your partner know what you lost and what to do if your pet is found? Add more words if you need to.

Sharing

Put your ad on a bulletin board in your classroom.

Making Hidden Pictures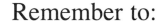

You have read about all kinds of animals. Some live on land, and some live in water. Today you and a friend will draw a picture together. Then you will hide some animals in your picture.

Remember to:

♦ Take turns sharing ideas.

♦ Use quiet voices when you talk.

First, get the things you will need to make your picture. Talk about what to draw. Then draw the picture together. When your picture is done, hide some animals in it. Can a friend find the animals you hide?

100 ♦ *Cooperative Learning*

The Cat in the Hat by Dr. Seuss *(Random House, 1957)*. A special ''cat'' who wears a tall red and white striped hat visits two children on a rainy day.

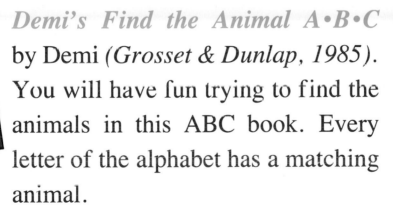

Demi's Find the Animal A•B•C by Demi *(Grosset & Dunlap, 1985)*. You will have fun trying to find the animals in this ABC book. Every letter of the alphabet has a matching animal.

17 Kings and 42 Elephants by Margaret Mahy *(Dial Books, 1987)*. Follow 17 kings and 42 elephants as they walk through the jungle singing. Several jungle animals join in the fun.

LET'S PRETEND

Sometimes it's fun to pretend.

How can a story help you pretend?

FRENCH TIN TOYS, c. 1898

I Want to Be Big, NOW!

written by Bernard Wiseman

Friends help each other.
June's friends help her pretend.

June was sad. "The kids over there say that I can't play with them. I think they're being rude," she said. "They say that I am too little. I wish I could be bigger."

"Can't you wait?" said Pat. "Our moms were little. Our dads were little, too. Now they are big. If you wait, you'll get big, too."

"But I don't want to wait,"
said June. "I want to be big NOW!"

"I know how to help you,"
said Jeff. "Come with me to my house."

Jeff got out some food.

"Here," said Jeff. "Eat all of this. My dad always tells me if I eat all my vegetables, I will grow to be big and strong. Maybe if you eat all of this, you'll get bigger and stronger faster."

"There," she said. "I can't eat any more. But I don't feel any bigger!"

"You don't look any bigger," said Greg.

"But I want to be big NOW," said June.

"I know what we can do," said Pat. "We can help you to look big. Come with me."

"Here, June. Put on
my mom's things," said Pat.
"Now you look big! See?"

"See?" said June. "I can't see!
The hat is over my eyes. I could fall.
This won't work!"

"I know," said Greg.
"Come with me."

"Here," said Greg. "Stand
on these. These will make you
big."

"I can see that I am bigger,"
said June. "But they are hard to
walk with. It will be hard to ride
my bicycle. These won't work. Maybe
I was wrong. Maybe I can't be
big now."

"My gram always tells me that it takes a big person to admit when she's wrong," said Pat.

"You know what that means, June?" said Jeff. "You ARE big, and you are big NOW!"

 ## What Do You Think?

Do you think June had good friends? Tell why or why not.

110

I Want to Be Big, NOW!

Questions

1. What three steps did June's friends take to try to help her?
2. Why didn't eating or dressing up help June to be bigger?
3. Did June show that she was big? How do you know this?

Writing to Learn

THINK AND DISCOVER June thought trying on a grown-up's clothes made her look older. Draw a picture to show what you would look like in a grown-up's clothes.

WRITE Look at your picture. Do you feel older? Write how you feel.

Then

When you can catch
And throw a ball,
And spell
Cat,
Dog,
And Pig,
Then you have finished
Being small
And started
Being Big.

Dorothy Aldis

112

The End

When I was One,
I had just begun.

When I was Two,
I was nearly new.

When I was Three,
I was hardly Me.

When I was Four,
I was not much more.

When I was Five,
I was just alive.

But now I am Six, I'm as clever as clever.
So I think I'll be six now for ever and ever.

A.A. Milne

Meet a boy who wonders what it would be like to be something else.

If I Were

by Katherine Page

If I were a coral reef, I'd be home
for a school of fish. All around me
I would see a rainbow of red, orange,
yellow, and blue.

The fish could live in my
caves. In my deep caves they would
be safe. Sand and shells would be
at my feet.

In my coral arms I would hold
bits of gold.

If I were a book, I'd be big
and fat. I would take people who
read me over the seas, and over
the mountains! My readers would
see many new people and things.

If my readers got tired, they
could stop and put me down. If
they needed a friend, they could read
me again.

If I were a flower, I'd be deep
blue. I would go over the land like
a blanket.

The ant and the beetle could use my leaves for their homes. The spider would make a web between my arms. I'd let the butterfly sit on my shoulder.

If I were a tree, I'd be
a tall pine. I'd be so fat and tall
that people could walk between
my feet.

Nine birds, five raccoons, and six squirrels would nest in my arms. The mother bear would use my shoulder to look for her cubs.

If I were a building, I'd be the tallest one around. I'd stand strong and tall.

From the top of me, people could see mountains, rivers, and seas. On clear days they could see the ships at sea. They could see trucks going over the land. I would help people see their world.

 What Do You Think?

Would you like to be any of the things in the story? Tell why or why not.

If I Were

 Questions

1. What things did the writer want to be?
2. How were the coral reef, the flower, and the tree like people?
3. What sounds might a tree hear? Why do you think this?

 Writing to Learn

THINK AND PRETEND   Have you ever pretended to be a flower, a tree, a car, or a crayon? Think about a thing that you would like to be. Draw a picture of it.

WRITE   Take your sheet of paper and finish the sentence below.

If I were a ____,

I would _____.

Vocabulary:

Word Groups

Read these words from "If I Were."

coral reef   sand   fish   shells

How are the words alike? They are names of things found in the sea.

Some words tell about the same kinds of things. These things can belong in the same group.

Read these words.

ant   milk   beetle   spider

Which word does not belong in the group? Tell why.

Look at the picture.

1. What animals do you see?
2. What plants do you see?
3. What red things do you see?
4. What other things in the picture can you put into a group?

In many games, you have to pretend. These children pretend to see a dinosaur.

The Story Game

by Steven Kroll

I was on my way
to get some peaches,
and I heard a yell from
Jimmy's house. So I ran to
his house and there were Jimmy
and Peggy and Lee and a big
tyrannosaurus stuck on the stairs.
Everyone pulled and pushed and
pushed and pulled.
Then, the tyrannosaurus sneezed
and everyone flew out the door.
    And Rusty said . . .

I was waiting
for the bus,
and Jimmy and Peggy
and Lee and Billy and
Alice and the tyrannosaurus
and I all got on.
Everyone else had
to get off.

And Stuart said. . .

RUSTY

STUART

I was
on the seesaw
at the park,
and this tyrannosaurus
came running up and
sat down on the other end
and I flew into the air
and landed on his back.
      And Joanne said . . .

STUART

JOANNE

134

I was <u>across</u> the park
on the swings,
and Jimmy and Peggy
and all of my friends
came dashing by
with a tyrannosaurus.
And I jumped off
and ran after them.
    And Lee said . . .

136

And then
the police came
and looked all over
the city,
but the tyrannosaurus
was gone!

What Do You Think?

Tell which part of the children's story was your favorite.

The Story Game

 Questions

1. What did Joanne see?
2. How are these words alike: *Jimmy, Rusty, Lee,* and *Billy*?
3. If you were playing this game, what would you pretend to see?
4. The children were playing a game of pretend. How do you know?

 Writing to Learn

THINK AND PRETEND
The children in " The Story Game " saw a tyrannosaurus. What animal would you like to see in a story? Draw a picture.

WRITE Tell about your picture. Write three things that your animal can do.

Pirate Story

by Robert Louis Stevenson

Three of us afloat
in the meadow
by the swing,

Three of us aboard
in the basket
on the lea.

Winds are in the air,
they are blowing
in the spring;

And waves are on the meadow
like the waves
there are at sea.

Hippo wants to make a wish. His friends give him some ideas.

Hippo Makes a Wish

written by Mike Thaler
illustrated by Maxie Chambliss

Hippo opened his eyes.
"Today I would like
to make a wish," he said.
Hippo thought and thought and thought.
But he could not think of what
to wish for.

So he got out of the river
and went to see Snake.

"Snake," said Hippo,

"Today I would like to make a wish.

But I don't know what to wish for."

"Wish for bright colors, like mine,"

said Snake.

Hippo closed his eyes.

He saw himself with bright colors.

Hippo opened his eyes.

"I don't think so," he said.

And he went to see Monkey.

"Monkey," said Hippo,
"Today I would like to make a wish.
But I don't know what to wish for."
"Wish for a long tail like mine,"
said Monkey.
"Then we could swing
in the trees together."
"That's true," said Hippo.
Hippo closed his eyes.
He saw himself
swinging in the trees.
"I don't think so," he said.
And he went to see Lion.

"Wish for a mane
just like mine," said Lion.
Hippo saw himself
with a mane like Lion's.
"I don't think so," Hippo said,
and he went to see Giraffe.

"Wish for a neck like mine,"
said Giraffe.
"You could see the tops of trees."
"That's true," said Hippo.
Hippo saw himself
with a long neck like Giraffe's.
"I don't think so," said Hippo,
and he went to see Elephant.

147

"I know!" said Elephant.
"Wish for a nose just like mine."
Hippo saw himself
with a long nose.
"I don't think so," he said,
and he went back to the river.

Hippo closed his eyes.

" What are you doing? " asked Mole.

" I am wishing, " said Hippo.

" What are you wishing for? " asked Mole.

"I am wishing to stay
just as I am," said Hippo
as he opened his eyes.
Mole looked at Hippo.
Hippo looked at Mole.
"Your wish has come true," said Mole.

What Do You Think?

What would you have told Hippo
to wish for if you had been his friend?

Hippo Makes a Wish

 ## Questions

1. Whom did Hippo see first? Whom did he see last?
2. Where did Hippo live? What tells you this?
3. Why did Hippo wish to stay as he was?

 ## Writing to Learn

THINK AND PLAN Hippo wanted to make a wish. You can make a wish, too. Take out a sheet of paper and draw a "wish" on it.

WRITE What did you wish? Write a sentence about your wish.

151

THE WORLD OF READING

Words Are All Around

Have you ever noticed that no matter where you go, you almost always see words?

There are words on signs and boxes.

SCHOOL BUS

55 POLICE

There are words on cars and trucks.

MOVING

FURNITURE

Bakery

You can even see words on balloons!

Words are all around us.

HAPPY BIRTHDAY

© 1985 PBC

David McPhail

David McPhail makes picture books. He makes up the story and the drawings, too.

"I started to draw when I was two," Mr. McPhail said. "I drew pictures on brown bags. I drew pictures on anything I could find at home and at school."

Mr. McPhail said, "My mother liked my drawings a lot. She would hang them up around the house. My mother told my sister and brothers that we could be anything we wanted to be!"

Mr. McPhail has a house in New England. "I like books, tall trees, the warm sun, and the blue sky," he said. "I do not like snow, ice, and TV."

"I always have new stories in my mind," Mr. McPhail said. "When I sit in my car, I may think of anything. I may think of a pig in a truck. I may think of bears."

"One time I wanted to make a picture book about a bear. I made many drawings of bears," said Mr. McPhail.

When you read the next story, you will see some of Mr. McPhail's pictures of bears. After you have read it, you may want to look for some of his other books:

Henry Bear's Park
Pig Pig Grows Up
Adam's Smile

 What Do You Think?

Would you like to draw pictures like David McPhail? Tell why.

LEE BENNETT HOPKINS INTERVIEWS
David McPhail

Questions

1. How does David McPhail make picture books?
2. Do you think David McPhail would like to live where it is always cold? How do you know?
3. In what way did David McPhail's mother help him to be who he is today?

Writing to Learn

THINK AND CHOOSE David McPhail likes books, tall trees, the warm sun, and the blue sky. What do you like? Draw a picture of some of the things you like.

WRITE Label the things in your picture.

159

Pretend that it is night. You go to your window and you see a bear!

The Bear's Toothache

written and illustrated
by David McPhail

One night something came to my window.
It was a bear with a toothache.

I went to the window and asked him in.

I looked at his teeth.
When I saw the one that ached,
I tried to pull it out.
It wouldn't come out.

"Maybe some meat will help it
come out," said the bear.
So we went down to the kitchen,
where the bear ate some meat.
The bear ate and ate.

But the tooth wouldn't come out.

When we got back to my room,
I tried to pull the tooth.
I tried to hit it with my pillow.
But the bear ducked, and I hit the lamp.
It fell.

My dad woke up and came to my room.
"What did you do to the lamp?"
he asked.

"It fell," I said.

"Oh," he said,
and he went back to bed.

I tried one more way
to pull the tooth.
I put my rope on the bear's tooth
and on the bed.

Then the bear went to the window.
He jumped out.

And just as he hit the ground,
the tooth came out!

The bear was so glad
that he gave me the tooth.

I put it under my pillow.

What Do You Think?

Would you have let the bear in
your room? Tell why or why not.

The Bear's Toothache

 ## Questions

1. How did the child try to get the bear's tooth out?
2. What happened when the bear jumped out of the window with the rope on his tooth?
3. If the boy had not opened the window, what might have happened? What makes you think so?

 ## Writing to Learn

THINK AND REMEMBER Draw a picture to show what might happen if you lost a tooth.

WRITE Tell about your picture.

By Myself

written by Eloise Greenfield
illustrated by Diane and Leo Dillon

When I'm by myself
And I close my eyes
I'm a twin
I'm a dimple in a chin
I'm a room full of toys
I'm a squeaky noise
I'm a gospel song
I'm a gong
I'm a leaf turning red
I'm a loaf of brown bread
I'm a whatever I want to be
An anything I care to be
And when I open my eyes
What I care to be
Is me

170

171

Comprehension:
Retelling a Story

Every story has a beginning, a middle, and an end.

Think about the story "The Bear's Toothache." How would you tell the story to a friend?

Use the chart below to help you remember what happened first, second, and last.

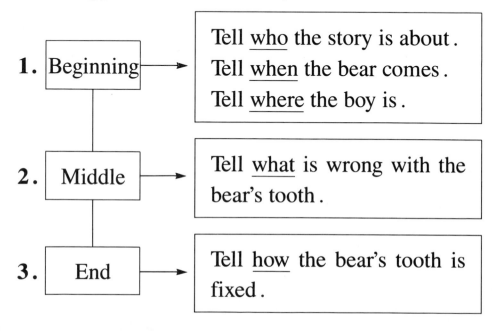

1. Beginning → Tell <u>who</u> the story is about.
Tell <u>when</u> the bear comes.
Tell <u>where</u> the boy is.

2. Middle → Tell <u>what</u> is wrong with the bear's tooth.

3. End → Tell <u>how</u> the bear's tooth is fixed.

Using What You Have Learned

Think about the story "The Three Little Pigs."
Use the chart below to retell the story to your class.

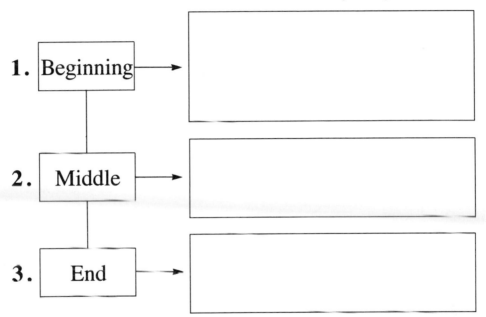

1. Beginning
2. Middle
3. End

Retell other stories you know. Be sure to tell the beginning, the middle, and the end of your story.

Melissa likes to pretend.
Sometimes her mom and dad
pretend, too.

Melissa's Friend Kim

by Christel Kleitsch

"Good morning, Mom," said Melissa.

"Good morning, Melissa," said Mom.

"Say good morning to Kim,"
said Melissa.

"Who's Kim?" asked Mom.

"This is Kim. She's over here,"
said Melissa.

"Oh, I see," said Mom.
"Good morning, Kim."

"Watch out, Dad," said Melissa.
"Please, don't sit there."

"Why not?" asked Dad.

"Kim is sitting there," said Melissa.

"Who's Kim?" said Dad.

"This is my friend, Kim," said Melissa.
"She's going to eat breakfast with us."

"It's nice to meet you, Kim," said Dad.

"Mom, may Kim have some breakfast?"
asked Melissa.

"Let her have some of yours, Melissa," said Mom.

"Kim can't have this for breakfast," said Melissa.

"She can't?" said Mom. "What can Kim have for breakfast?"

"She told me she has dandelion pie," said Melissa.

"Dandelion pie for breakfast?" said Mom.

"Oh, yes," said Melissa.

"Didn't I get a dandelion pie just the other day?" said Dad.

"Yes, you did." said Mom. "Would you both like some?"

"I believe I'll pass," said Dad.

"Both Kim and I would love some," said Melissa.

"Thanks, Mom," Melissa said. "This is good!"

"May Kim come for lunch tomorrow?" said Melissa.

"Sure she can," said Mom. "I'll make you both some spinach sandwiches."

"Spinach sandwiches?" said Melissa.

"Yes," said Mom. "Kim told me that's what she eats for lunch."

"Oh, no!" said Melissa. Then they all laughed.

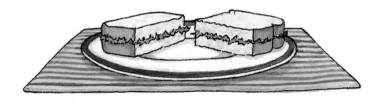

 ## What Do You Think?

Do you think Melissa and her parents had fun? Tell why or why not.

Melissa's Friend Kim

 ## Questions

1. Why did Dad start to sit where Kim sat?
2. How did Melissa's mom surprise her?
3. Where do you think Melissa's dad got the dandelion pie?
4. Could Kim be a real person? What makes you think so?

 ## Writing to Learn

THINK AND PRETEND Think about what Melissa and Kim might say when they are given spinach sandwiches.

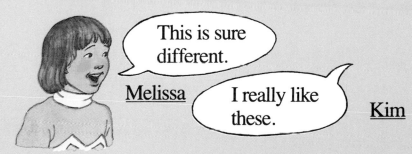

Melissa: This is sure different.

Kim: I really like these.

WRITE Copy the speech balloons. Write the words for Melissa and Kim.

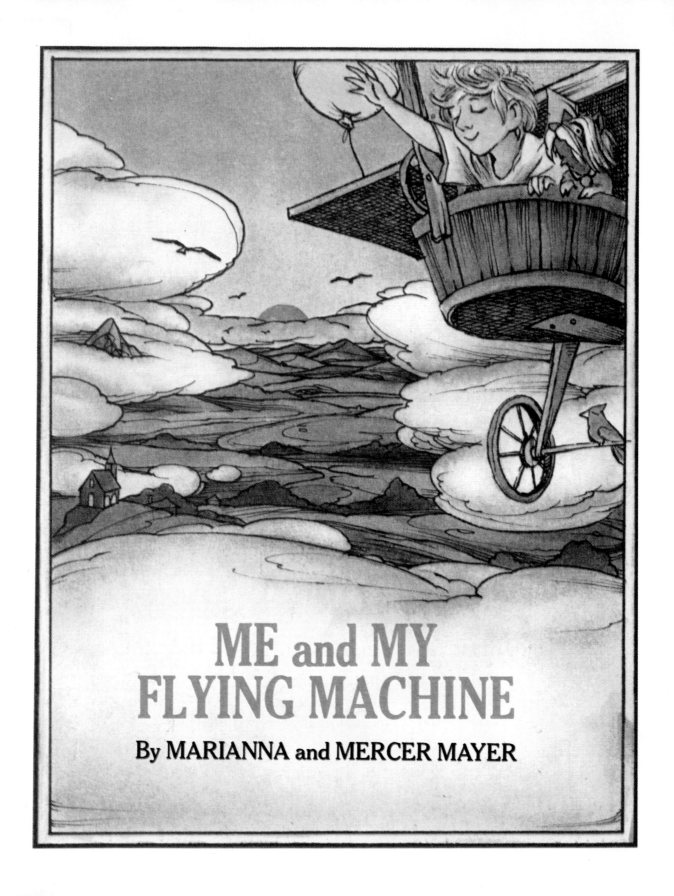

ME and MY
FLYING MACHINE

By MARIANNA and MERCER MAYER

Last summer I discovered an old
barn. It was full of great things.

There were boxes, pieces of wood.
There were even nails and a hammer.
I could build anything I wanted.
I'll build a flying machine, I thought,
and I started building.
I worked all day.

My flying machine was almost
finished but it was dinner time and I had
to wash the dog.

So I closed up the barn for the night. "Good-bye, flying machine. I'll finish you tomorrow," I said and went home.

That night I dreamed about my flying machine and how it would look when I was finished. It would be something tremendous. Smaller than a castle but bigger than a truck.

I finally decided on something smaller.
Besides, it would take me too long
to build a big flying machine.

There were so many things I could do.
I'd deliver mail to Eskimos and people
who never get mail.

I'd fly above the fog and rescue lost
boats at sea.

I'd carry mountain climbers to the
mountain top. So they wouldn't have
to spend so much time climbing.

Birds could rest on the wings, if they
were tired from flying around all day.

From high in my flying machine I could
see everything. So I'd always know where
everything was and I'd never get lost.

My flying machine would win first prize in every race.

And soon I'd have so many medals and trophies that I wouldn't know where to keep them.

I couldn't wait to finish my flying
machine. The next day I ran all the way
to the old barn.

Everything was just like I left it.

There was more work to do so I
nailed on another wing and some stuff.

I finished working on my flying
machine but somehow it didn't look quite
the way I thought it would.

There was a brush and some old
paint cans lying around. So I used a little
of each. It was just what my flying
machine needed.

It looked better than I had imagined.
So I tied a rope on the front end to
pull my flying machine outside to dry.

It creaked and moaned
and started to shake as I pulled.

And then before I could pull it out of
the barn . . . my flying machine
fell apart.

Tomorrow I'll build a rowboat.

 What Do You Think?

If you found a barn filled with
wood and things, what would you build?

Writing About a Make-Believe Friend

You read about Melissa and her make-believe friend, Kim. Pretend you have a make-believe friend.

Getting Ready

Close your eyes and think about your make believe friend.

♦ Is it a boy or a girl or a pet?

♦ How old is your friend?

♦ What does your make-believe friend look like?

Writing

Open your eyes and draw what you saw. Then write about your friend. Copy and finish the sentences below.

My make-believe friend's name is _____.
I like my friend because _____.
My friend looks like _____.
My friend and I like to _____.

Listening to My Writing

Read what you wrote to a partner. Would you like to write anything more about your make-believe friend?

Sharing

Paste your picture and your writing onto a large sheet of paper. Show your story to your classmates.

Planning a Play Without Words

Today you and a friend can work together. You will put on a play that does not have words.

Remember to:

♦ Listen to your friend's ideas.

♦ Help each other practice.

Now think of some things that the play could be about. You might pretend to bake a cake or play a game like catch. Together decide on one idea for your play.

Practice what you will do. Remember that this is a play without words!

If You Take a Pencil by Fulvio Testa *(Dial Press, 1982)*. This book will take you on an adventure. Look at the pictures *very* carefully, and then you can draw your own story.

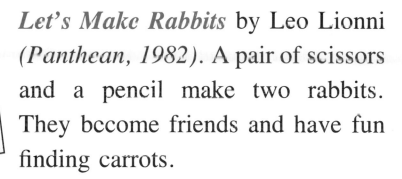

Let's Make Rabbits by Leo Lionni *(Panthean, 1982)*. A pair of scissors and a pencil make two rabbits. They become friends and have fun finding carrots.

Where the Wild Things Are by Maurice Sendak *(Harper & Row, 1963)*. Max is sent to his room because he has jumped around in his wolf suit. But Max wants to go where the wild things are and become king!

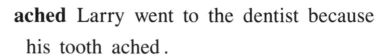

ached ◇ anything

A

ached Larry went to the dentist because his tooth ached.

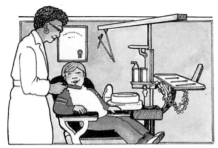

Larry's tooth **ached.**

across The dog ran across the road.

admit I admit that Lani runs faster than I do.

after Jane helps around the house after school.

again It rained every day this week. It will rain again today.

always We always visit Grandma on the weekend.

animals Sue loves dogs, cats, birds, and other animals.

Sue loves **animals.**

any Liz didn't want any milk.

anything When he was sick, Sean didn't eat anything all day.

arms Jean swings her arms as she walks.

as Janet sang as she played.

asked Mark asked for help.

ate The dog ate everything in his dish.

away Mary went away for the day.

arms

B

beetle The beetle hid under a leaf.

believe Do you believe that dogs can fly?

bench The old man sat on the bench.

between Don sits between Peg and Jan.

bigger A truck is bigger than a car.

blanket The red blanket was on the bed.

blew The wind blew the man's hat off.

blow Lin will blow out the candles.

books The teacher has lots of books.

born The tiny kittens were born yesterday.

both Both Susan and John are six years old.

breakfast It is time for breakfast.

breaks Glass breaks if it is dropped.

bright Red and purple are bright colors.

asked

blanket

blow

building

butterfly

closed

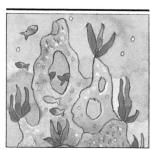
coral reef

brown The house is painted brown.

building Diane lives in a big building.

butterfly The butterfly flew past the red rose.

by Vito must be home by dinnertime.

C

calf The cow licked her calf.

cannot The hen cannot find her eggs.

chin Alma has milk on her chin.

chinny Not by the hair on my chinny chin chin.

city They live on a farm. We live in a city.

clear It is so clear today that you can see a long way.

close Abe lives close to Ruth's house.

closed The shops are always closed on Sundays.

colors The drawing has many colors in it.

coral reef Fish swim around this coral reef.

corncob After you eat corn, the corncob is left.

cows The cows give the farmer lots of milk.

corncob

D

---

dandelion Jane sat on the grass and picked a dandelion.

door The door was wide open.

draw Rick likes to draw trees.

drawings Jane makes drawings of cats with her pencil.

drew Jane drew four cats on her paper with her crayon.

dandelion

draw

E

---

eat Bears eat lots of fish.

else Bob is still hungry. He wants something else to eat.

everyone Everyone in my class likes to read.

eyes Juan has brown eyes.

eat

F

farm

food

friend

farm Carmen saw pigs and hens at the farm.

farmer The farmer lives on the farm.

fast Kim ran very fast.

first It was the first time that Rosa had seen snow.

flew The duck flew away.

flower That flower is from my garden.

fly I wish I could fly like a bird.

food The birds have food to eat.

friend Carmen is Juan's best friend.

from Jane walked away from the shop.

fur My cat has very soft fur.

G

gold

game The children made up a new game.

going Mr. Smith is going to work.

gold My mother's ring is made of gold.

gone The rabbits have gone into their hole.

good The good king sent away the bad dragon.

ground Greg planted seeds in the ground.

grow Susan wants to grow long hair like Sharon's.

ground

H

hair Maria likes to brush her hair.

hard It is hard to stand on your head.

heard Rob heard the dog bark.

hill Jack and Jill climbed up the hill.

himself José was talking to himself.

hole The boy dug a large hole.

house That house is where I live.

hill

hole

I

ice Everyone went skating on the ice.

ice

203

lamp

J

just The cat just spilled the milk a minute ago.

K

kinds The shop sells many kinds of cheese.

kitchen We eat lunch in the kitchen.

knock Dad began to knock on the door.

laughed

L

lamp When it gets dark, we will turn on the lamp.

laughed The children laughed at the clown.

leaps The cat leaps onto the table.

leaves We rake leaves in the fall.

liked Tom liked his new friend.

little The baby's shirt is very little.

leaps

leaves

love Mary and Tom love their baby sister.
lunch Meg ate her lunch with Norma.

M

lunch

many There are many animals on a farm.
meadows The cows were eating grass in
the meadows.
mind "I don't mind if I'm last in the
race," said Joe.
more The kitten wanted more food.

meadows

N

---

nest The birds made a nest.
new Gail's old coat was too small. She
just got a new one.
next Dave gets off the bus at the next
stop.
night We all go to sleep at night.
nose My dog has a big wet nose.
now It is raining now.

nest

O

opened

old This house has been here for a long time. It is very old.

opened Father opened the letter.

orange Beth picked out a big orange pumpkin.

our We live here. This is our house.

outside Mother was in the shop. We waited outside.

P

park

peaches

park Lisa went to the park to play.

peaches I like to eat peaches and cream.

people You can see lots of people at the shops.

person We need another person for our team.

pie Kim made an apple pie.

pillow Tom likes a soft pillow for his head.

pie

please "Please, can I go out to play?" asked Amanda.

pocket Mr. Long keeps a pen in his pocket.

police The police helped Sam when he was lost.

pulls Ed pulls his toy across the room.

purple Sara has a purple dress.

pushed Todd pushed the door open.

raccoons

R

race

rabbits Rabbits like to eat carrots.

raccoons Raccoons are wild animals.

race Chuck won the race.

rainbow You may see a rainbow if it rains as the sun comes out.

readers All readers like this book.

rivers It is fun to go boating on rivers.

room This room is the bedroom.

round A ball is round.

rude Sam never says "please" or "thank you." He is very rude.

rainbow

readers

running My father goes running every morning.

sandwiches

S

sandwiches I like to eat sandwiches for lunch.

saw I saw the sunset last night.

sees The cat sees the fish.

sheep The sheep are on the hill.

sheep

shoulder My cat likes to sit on my shoulder.

show Bob will show you how to swim.

sitting Sara was sitting on her bed.

sitting

small The big cat picked up the small kitten.

snow We get cold when we play in the snow.

snuggles The kitten snuggles up to his mother.

snuggles

some Liz picked six flowers. She had some flowers.

soon It is late. I want to go home soon.

spider The spider made a big web.

spinach Eating spinach makes you big and strong.

stairs Jo ran up the stairs.

start The race is ready to start.

ready to **start**

started Helen was late, and she started to run.

stays A pine tree stays green all year.

still The dentist told Jack to sit still.

stop You must stop for the red light.

stop

stories Joe liked all the stories his father read to him.

story My mother reads me a story before I go to bed.

straw Cows and horses eat straw.

Mother reads a **story.**

string Mike tied up the box with string.

strong The strong man lifted the big box.

sure Tom is sure that he is six years old.

T

thanks Sue gave us her thanks for the gift.

that I like that red box. I do not like that yellow one.

straw

209

things

thinking

Dad **told** me.

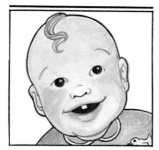

tooth

their We went to see our grandpa and grandma. Their house is smaller than ours.

them I like Fran and Mike. I want to be friends with them.

there We went to the beach. It was warm there.

these That book is not mine. These books are mine.

things I like to make things out of clay.

thinking Harriet was thinking about her new pet.

thought Robin thought of a gift for Tom.

three There were three little pigs.

tired After playing all day, Rosa felt very tired.

today Today is Sunday.

together The three of us finished the race together.

told Dad told me about the large birds.

tomorrow Today is Sunday. Tomorrow will be Monday.

took We took a walk with the dog.

tooth The little boy has a new tooth.

toothache Bob had a tooth that hurt. He had a toothache.

tried Jim tried to catch the bus.

true It is true that ducks can fly.

turtles Turtles can swim very well.

two The dish broke into two pieces.

turtles

---

u

---

under Ron sleeps under the blankets.

until We can play until it gets dark.

two pieces

---

v

---

vegetables The vegetables I like best are carrots and green beans.

very An ant is very small.

vegetables

---

w

---

wait Greg has to wait for the bus every day.

walk Grandpa can't run now, but he likes to walk.

Greg must **wait.**

211

watch

window

Pedro **won**
the contest.

want "I want a new book," said Sally.

wanted Yesterday, I wanted to go to the playground.

warm The sun feels warm.

watch The cat likes to watch birds.

were Three birds were sitting in the tree.

when The dog barks when we come home.

where I live here. Where do you live?

why Jim wanted to know why snow is white.

window My dog likes to look out of the window.

wise Grandma knows everything. She is very wise.

won Pedro won the fishing contest.

won't The dog and the cat won't play together.

work The toy truck broke. It does not work any more.

world The ship sailed around the world.

would Anna has a big sandwich. She would like to share it with Jeff.

wouldn't Pete wouldn't play with Ruff.

Anna **would** like to share.

Y

---

yellow The color of my cat is bright yellow.

you'll I will lend you my bat if you'll lend me your ball.

Pete **wouldn't** play.

yellow cat

WORD LIST

The following story critical words appear in *Make a Wish*. The words are listed next to the number of the page on which they first appear.

Unit 1

A Morning in Fall

11 farm
    when
    still

12 stays
    warm

13 cows

15 calf

16 sheep

Who Took the Farmer's Hat?

22 farmer
    old
    brown
    took
    away

24 hole

26 nest

28 new

A Rainbow for Sara

32 asked
    string

33 you'll

34 thinking

36 orange
    yellow
    purple

38 rainbow

Polar Bear Leaps

47 born
    first
    snow

48 as
    small
    ice
    breaks

50 leaps

The Three Little Pigs

56 three

57 straw
    house
    strong

58 knock
    friend

59 blow

60 blew

A World of Animals

69 world
    animals
    under
    ground

70 turtles

72 rabbits
    meadows

The Hare and the Tortoise

78 walk
    city
    park

79 fast

80 race

81 very
    stop

84 won

DOROTHY ALDIS

These authors have written some of the stories in this book.

DOROTHY ALDIS

Dorothy Aldis wrote many books, poems, and stories for young people. Her first book also had songs in it. Dorothy Aldis also wrote a true story. It was about the life of Beatrix Potter, who wrote the Peter Rabbit stories. As a young girl, she moved from Chicago to a farm. *(1896–1966)*

SARA COLERIDGE

Sara Coleridge lived in England. Her father was a famous poet. His name was Samuel Taylor Coleridge. Sara Coleridge was also a poet. She wrote poems to help her own children learn their lessons. The poems were collected into a book called <u>Pretty Lessons in Verse for Good Children.</u> *(1802–1852)*

SARA COLERIDGE

AILEEN FISHER

Aileen Fisher has written many poems and stories. She has won awards for her writing. Aileen Fisher says she has always loved the country. She grew up in the country. Now she lives in Colorado near a mountain. She likes to take a walk every day with her dog along the mountain trails. *(Born 1906)*

AILEEN FISHER

ELOISE GREENFIELD

Eloise Greenfield did not think she would be a writer when she grew up. She says, "I loved words, but I loved to read them, not write them. I loved their sounds." Now writing is an important part of her life. Eloise Greenfield has received the American Library Association Notable Book Award and many other awards. *(Born 1929)*

ELOISE GREENFIELD

STEVEN KROLL

Steven Kroll says, "I really love writing for children." When he writes, he tries to remember things about his own childhood. "When I write about a child's room, that room is often my own." He thinks it is important for writers to remember what it was like to be a child. *(Born 1941)*

STEVEN KROLL

MARIANNA MAYER

Marianna Mayer is a writer and illustrator. When she was little, she drew pictures for stories that her parents read to her. She decided to become an artist. She likes to illustrate fairy tales. She says working on fairy tales is "wonderful—they are my friends." *(Born 1945)*

MARIANNA MAYER

MERCER MAYER

Mercer Mayer is an author and illustrator. He has won many awards for his books. His first book was *A Boy, a Dog, and a Frog.* It was made into a movie. Mercer Mayer does not think of his books as being only for children. He says, "My books are for the children in all of us, really." *(Born 1943)*

MERCER MAYER

DAVID MCPHAIL

DAVID MCPHAIL

David McPhail illustrates books for children. He also writes books. David McPhail says he does not know what a picture will look like when he begins to draw it. "I have the feeling that if I could see very clearly what I wanted from the beginning, there would be no reason for me to draw." He is a Caldecott winner. *(Born 1940)*

A. A. MILNE

A. A. MILNE

Alan Alexander Milne wrote many stories and poems for children. Some of the stories are about a boy named Christopher Robin and a bear named Winnie-the-Pooh. A. A. Milne had one son. His name was also Christopher Robin. *(1882–1956)*

JOAN NODSET

Joan Nodset has written many books for children. She gets her ideas for her stories from different places. The idea for one of her books came from a dream she had. When she was growing up, her mother read to her almost every night. Joan Nodset says she wanted to be a writer for as long as she can remember.

JOAN NODSET

ROBERT LOUIS STEVENSON

Robert Louis Stevenson was born in Scotland. He was often sick when he was a little boy. When he grew up, he wrote poems and adventure stories for children. One of his books is called *Treasure Island.* He said that he made up the story for that book after he drew a map of a make-believe island. *(1850–1894)*

ROBERT LOUIS STEVENSON

ALFRED, LORD TENNYSON

Alfred Tennyson was a poet. He lived in England. The first poems he wrote were not very popular, but he kept on writing. He became very famous during his own lifetime. He was made official poet, or poet laureate, of England. He was also made a baron. After he was made a baron, he was called Lord Tennyson. *(1809–1892)*

ALFRED, LORD TENNYSON

MIKE THALER

Mike Thaler writes children's books. He also illustrates books. He has written more than sixty children's books. Some of his books are collections of riddles, jokes, and cartoons. Mike Thaler is also a songwriter and a sculptor. *(Born 1936)*

Author
INDEX

224